The British Museum

AROUND the WORLD Colouring BOOK

First published 2017 by Nosy Crow Ltd
The Crow's Nest, Baden Place, Crosby Row
London, SE1 1YW
www.nosycrow.com

ISBN 978 1 78800 000 0

Published in collaboration with the British Museum

A CIP catalogue record for this book is available from the British Library.

Printed in Turkey

1 3 5 7 9 8 6 4 2

The British Museum

AROUND the WORLD Colouring BOOK

illustrated by

THOMAS FLINTHAM

When you see a shape like this, it's time to start stickering!

Contents

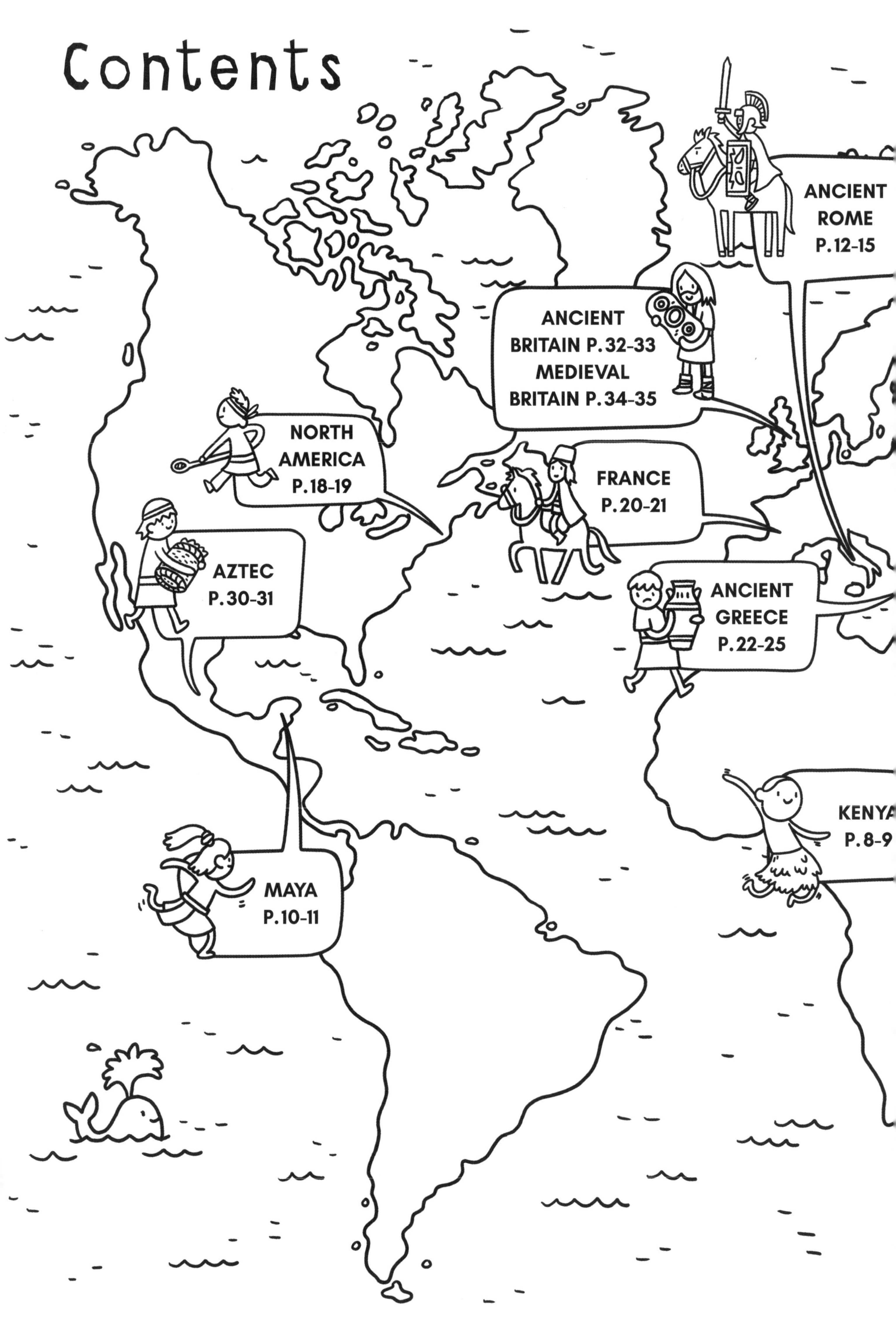

ANCIENT ROME P.12-15
ANCIENT BRITAIN P.32-33
MEDIEVAL BRITAIN P.34-35
NORTH AMERICA P.18-19
FRANCE P.20-21
AZTEC P.30-31
ANCIENT GREECE P.22-25
KENYA P.8-9
MAYA P.10-11

ANCIENT EGYPT P.2-5
CHINA P.6-7
JAPAN P.16-17
PERSIA P.28-29
SOLOMON ISLANDS P.38-39
INDIA P.36-37
THAILAND P.40-41
NEW ZEALAND P.26-27

Ancient Egypt

The ancient Egyptians built stunning temples on the banks of the River Nile. They were decorated with images of the Egyptian gods and there were often extravagant festivals held outside and on the river.

This statue has the head of a hawk and the body of a lion!

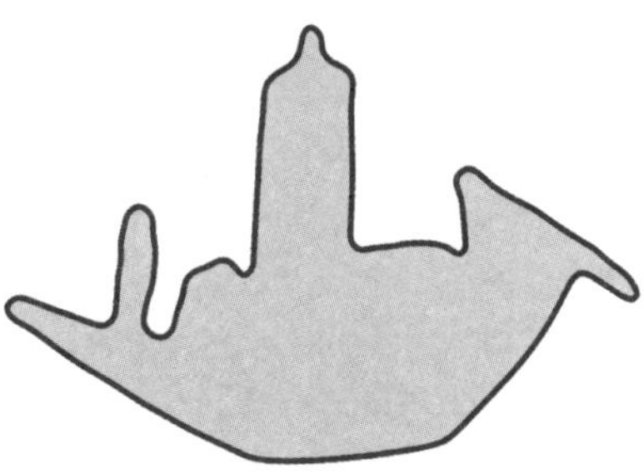

Wooden boats like this model sailed on the Nile.

Fruits, vegetables and spices were sold in baskets in the market.

This blue hippo figure is decorated with water plants.

Ancient Egypt

Thousands of years ago, the ancient Egyptians built pyramids as tombs for their kings and queens. Each pyramid was made from up to two million stone blocks and it took twenty men to move each one!

Sometimes animals were wrapped up as mummies too!

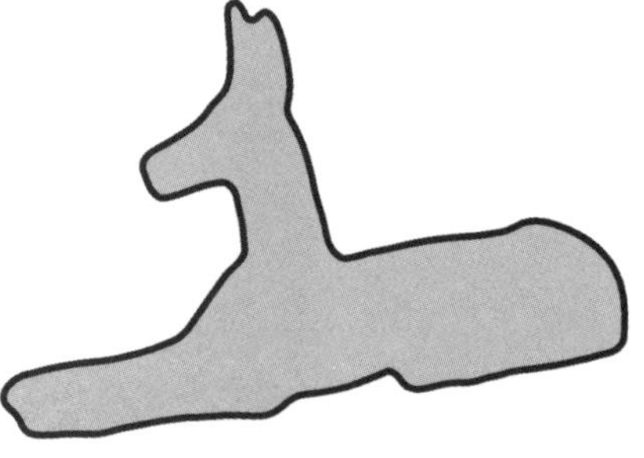

Anubis was a god who was often shown as a jackal.

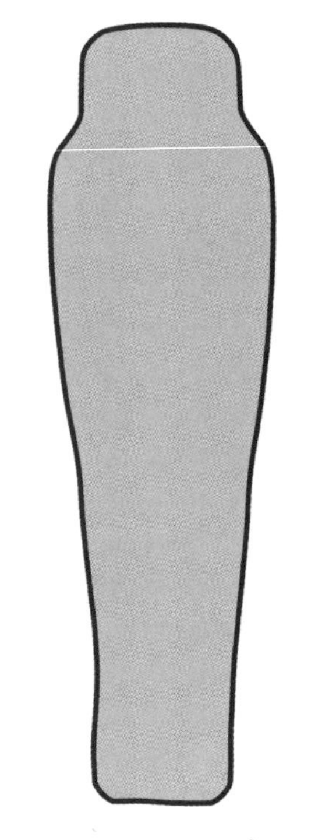

A mummy was kept inside a special case called a coffin.

China

The Forbidden City in Beijing was home to the Chinese emperors for five hundred years. Within the palace walls are hundreds of buildings with yellow roofs and red pillars. Thousands of people took care of the imperial family there.

This beautiful dish was made at China's porcelain capital Jingdezhen.

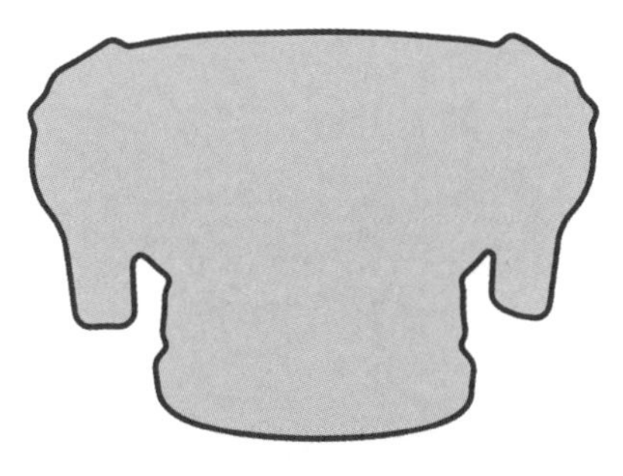

A *gui* is a type of bowl that was used for important ceremonies.

In China, dragons are symbols of power and strength.

Kenya

Africa is made up of lots of different countries and they each have their own traditions. The Kamba people live in Kenya in East Africa. They are well known for their carving skills and crafts. Some Kamba wear colourful beadwork ornaments and costumes at special festivals or ceremonies.

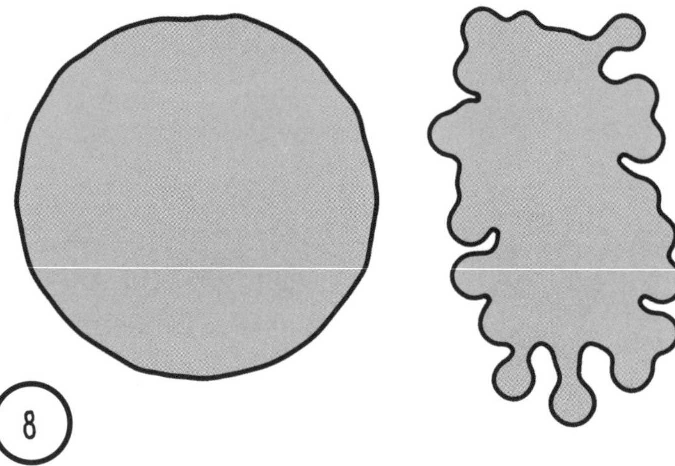

Girls and women wear necklaces made from glass beads – and sometimes copper coins!

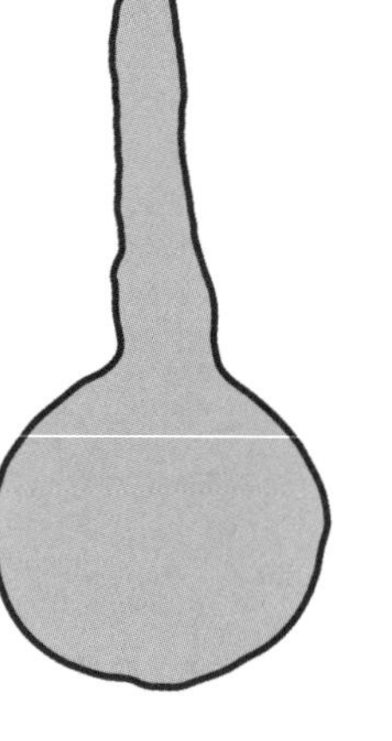

This gourd is decorated with glass beads and is used to serve porridge.

Recycled materials – such as the aluminium bells here – are used to make dance armlets.

Look at this amazing apron! It's made from colourful beads and copper chain.

This pot is decorated with hieroglyphs – pictures that represent words.

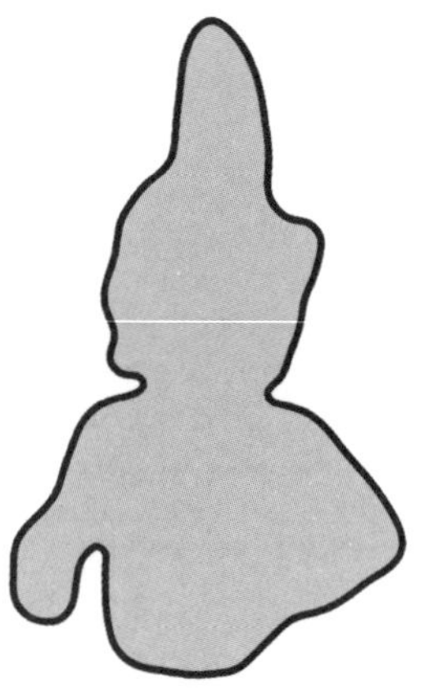

Here is a sculpture of the Maya god of the harvest.

The Maya often carved pictures into stone.

This painted pottery vase is over 1,200 years old!

Maya

In ancient Central America, Maya people built magnificent temples and palaces that reached up to the sky. They also had many religious rituals including dancing, music and sacred ball games. They played between steep stone walls with very heavy rubber balls!

Ancient Rome

The Roman army was one of the most powerful armies in history. It was made up of thirty legions – each with around 5,000 soldiers called legionaries. There were hundreds of forts all over the empire and each was built in a similar way. They all included toilets called lavatories, which comes from the Latin word *lavare*, meaning 'to wash'.

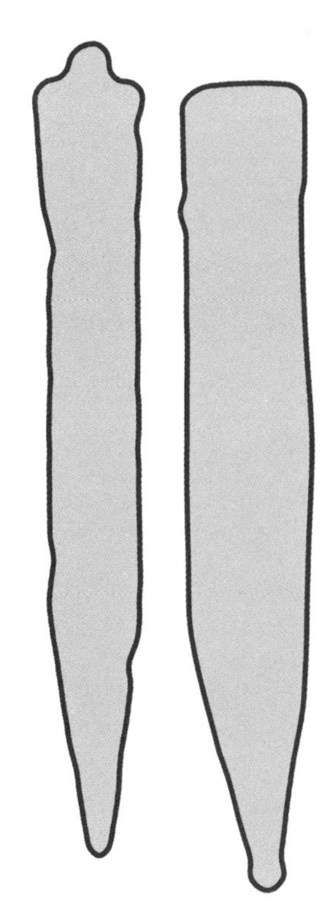

Roman swords were made from iron and often decorated.

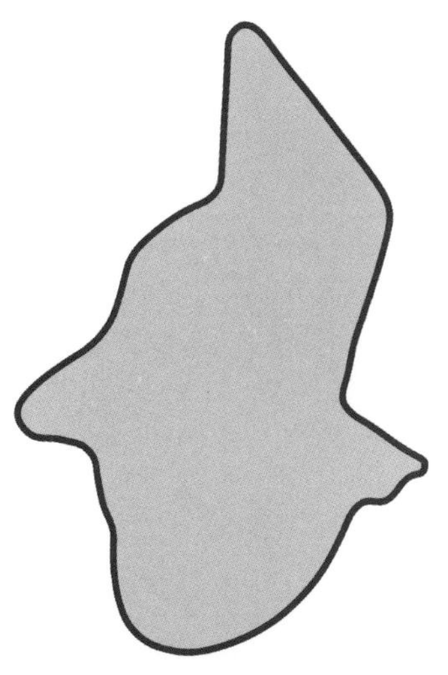

Gladiators wore helmets to protect them while fighting.

Ancient Romans wore leather sandals called *soleae*.

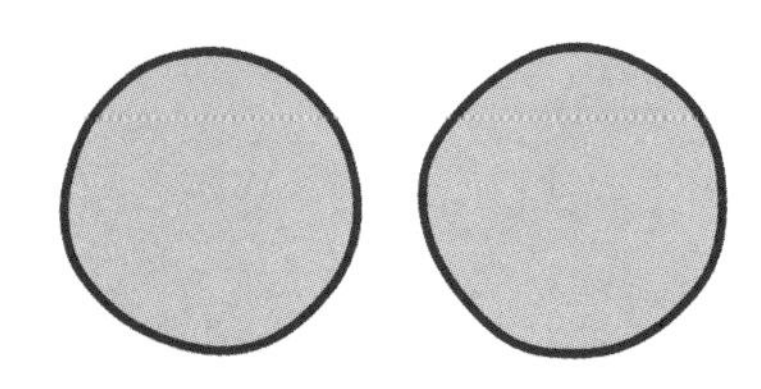

Roman coins had emperors' faces on them.

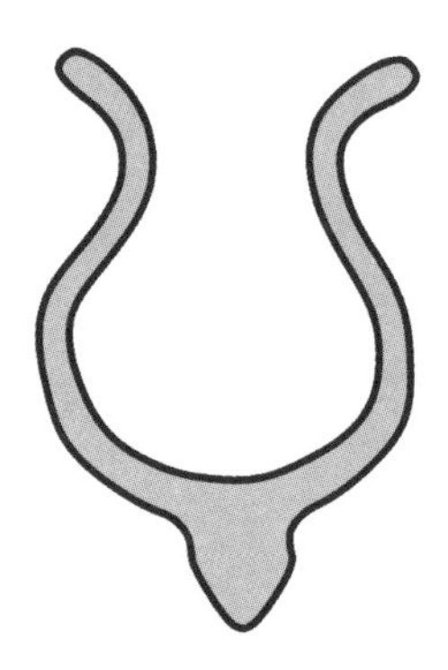

This gold necklace has a butterfly made from precious stones.

This is part of a mosaic pavement – a picture made from tiny tiles.

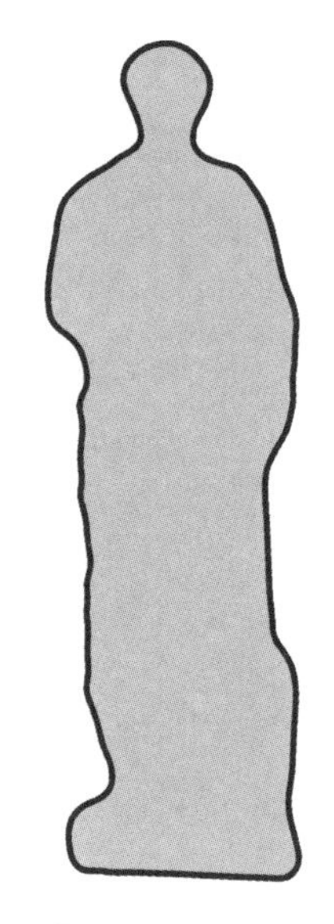

The Romans made statues of their emperors and senators, who were government leaders.

Ancient Rome

The Forum was an open space in the middle of ancient Rome that was first used as a market place. It was always very busy and bustling. With temples and shops all around it, the Forum was used for festivals and funerals, as well as business and politics.

日本

Japan

Japanese gardens are carefully designed, blending together different elements such as sand, rocks, water, plants and ornaments like lanterns and bamboo fences. Temples like this one are often surrounded by a beautiful landscape, which makes people feel calm.

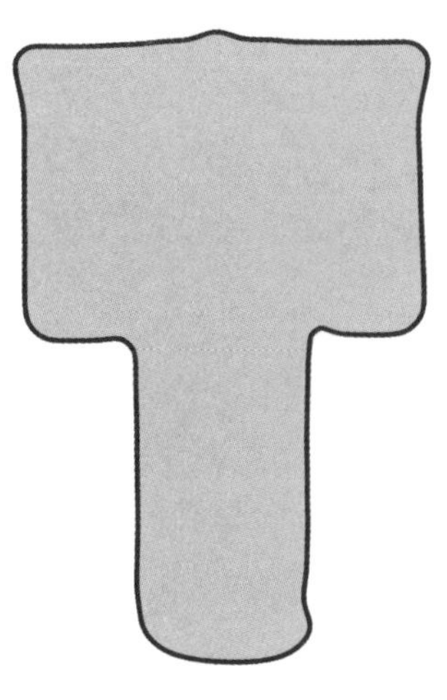

Traditional Japanese robes are called *kimonos*.

This is a woodblock print of Mount Fuji.

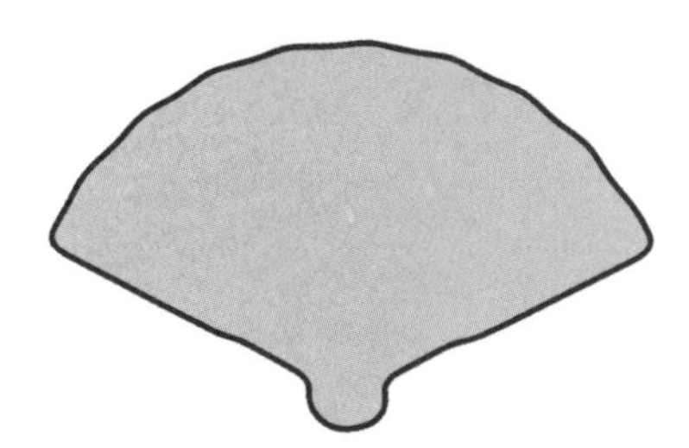

Look at this paper fan painted with ink.

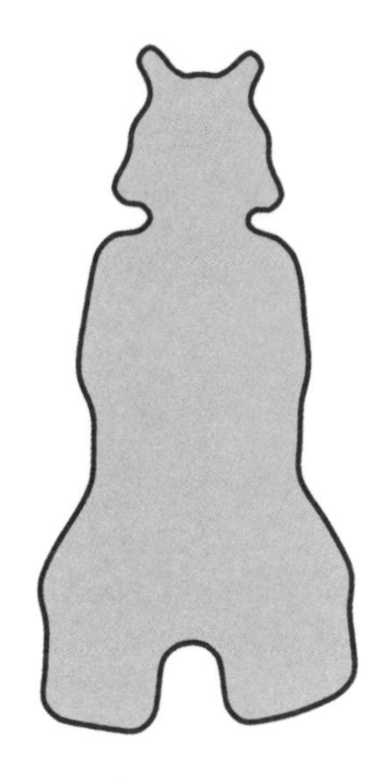

Samurais wore armour to protect them when they fought.

These leather moccasins have beads on them.

This tool is called a *tomawhawk*.

North America

Iroquois chiefs from six tribes would meet and make decisions together. In fact, they still meet today. Daily life included growing crops and hunting. Communities generally lived in a very large longhouse all together and they played a game called *lacrosse*.

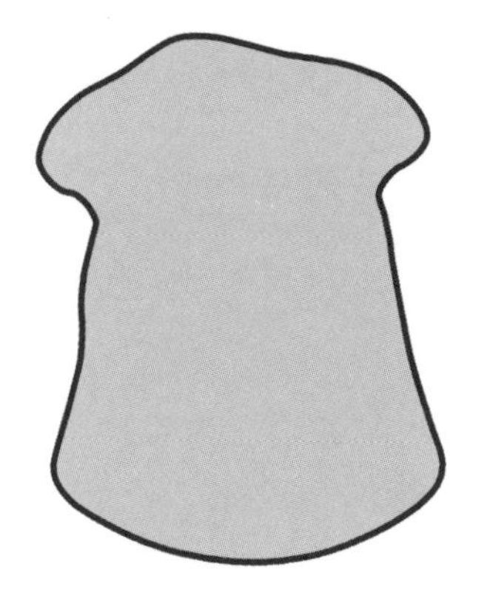

This black felt pouch is decorated with flowers.

Here is a basket made of black ash tree.

France

In medieval Europe, many people worked as farmers, growing crops such as barley, wheat and oats. They also had animals like chickens for eggs and cows for milk.

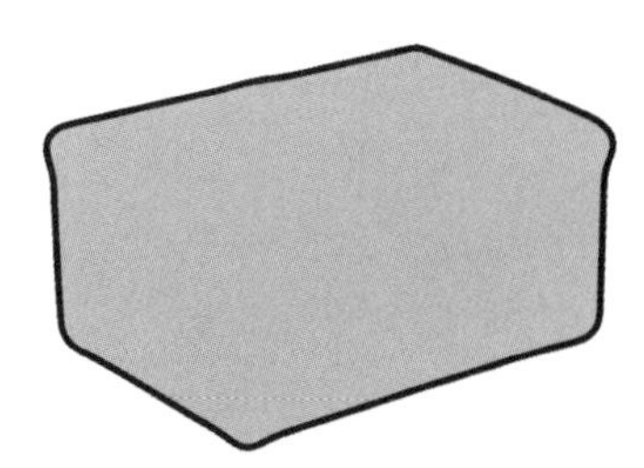

This box is decorated with ladies, knights, lions and hawks.

The Royal Gold Cup is made from solid gold!

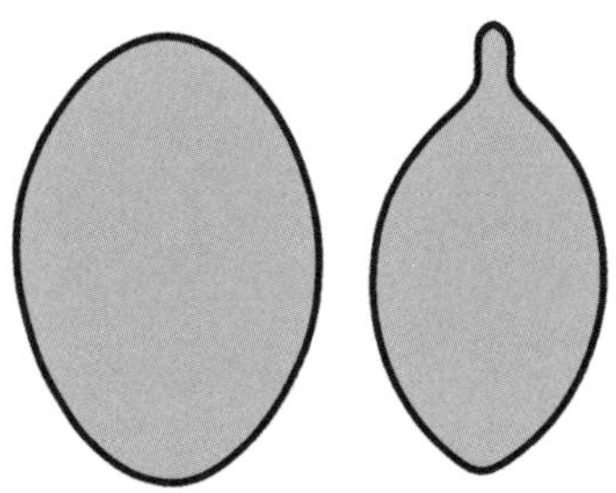

Seals made of melted wax were used on important papers.

This ivory mirror case has dragons and knights on it.

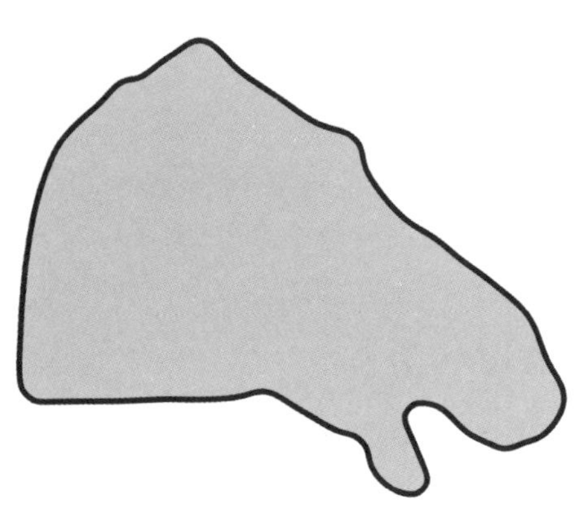

This marble horse head comes from the Parthenon.

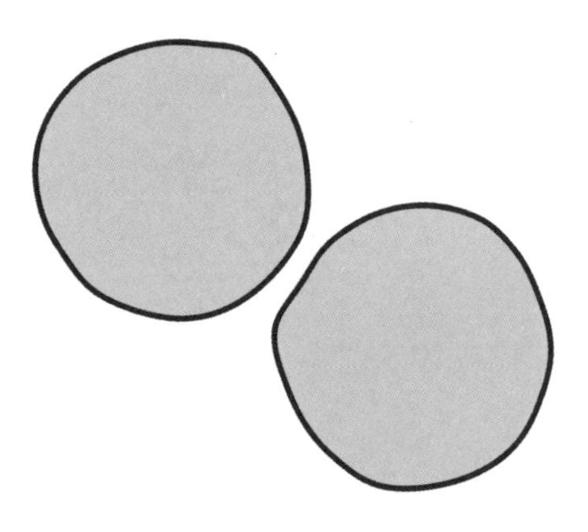

Greek coins sometimes had monster faces on them – like this gorgon!

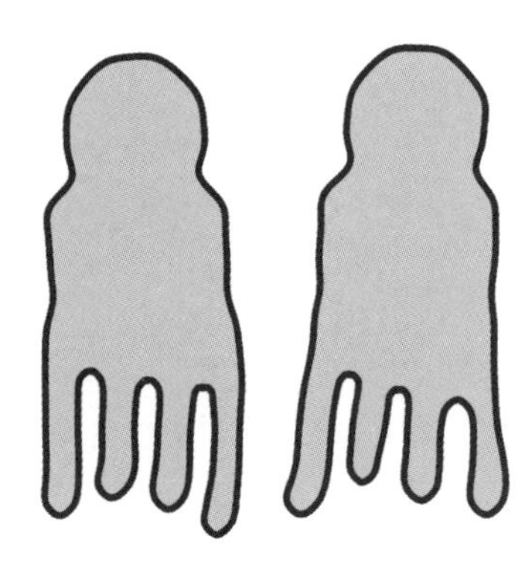

Here is a pair of gold earrings shaped like boats!

Ancient Greece

Athens was the richest city in ancient Greece. The wealthy people that lived there built a huge temple for the goddess Athena on top of a hill called the Acropolis. This temple was known as the Parthenon.

Ancient Greece

Ancient Greeks were also potty about pots! They used them for storing food and sold them in the markets. Plays were performed in large amphitheatres during religious festivals. Actors wore masks so that people in the audience could see what type of character they were playing.

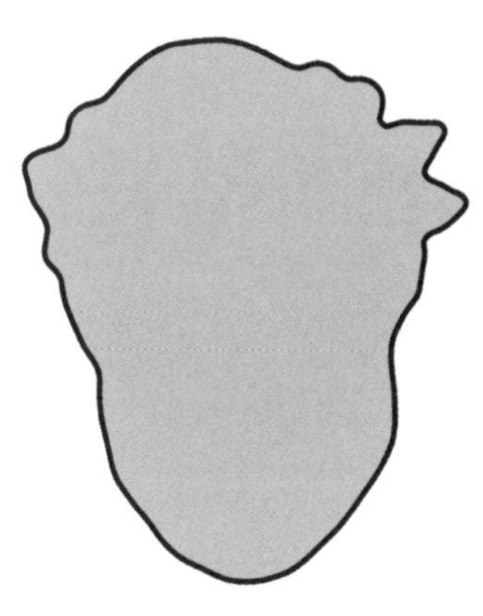

Look at this old man mask made from terracotta!

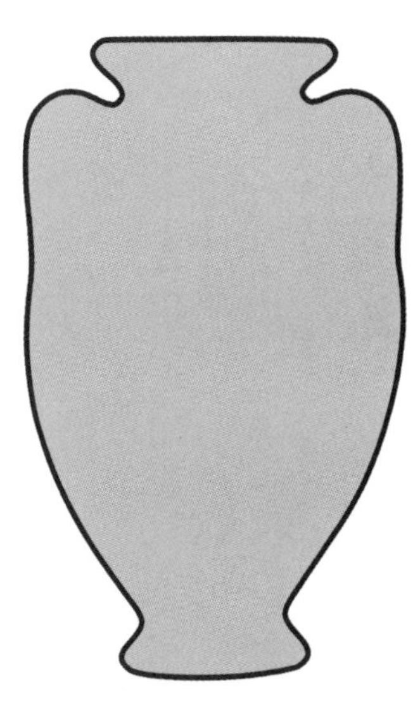

This is a Greek amphora – a tall jug with two handles and a narrow neck.

This vase has a siren on it – a bird with the head of a woman!

New Zealand

Oceania is a region that includes Australia, New Zealand and many other island groups. In New Zealand, Maori society is organised into tribes. Each group has a meeting house called a *wharenui*. Here, they hold special welcoming ceremonies called *powhiri* which include speeches, dances and singing.

Here is a greenstone hand weapon!

The big block that sits above a doorway is called a lintel – this one comes from a meeting house.

Maori cloaks have coloured woven borders and tassels made from dog hair.
This Maori kite is made from wood and feathers from all kinds of birds.

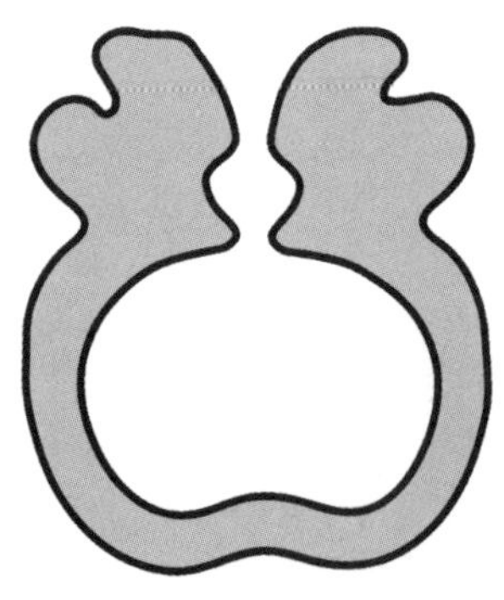

Here is a gold armlet from the Oxus Treasure.

Tiles were colourful and often showed scenes from history.

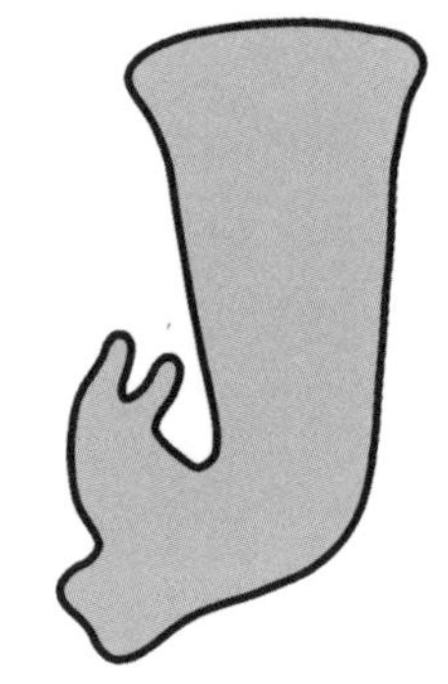

This is a silver drinking horn with a griffin on it.

This is a piece of stone from a Persian palace. It shows a sphinx, with the head of a woman and body of a lion!

Persia

Palaces in ancient Persia featured arches, domes and towers, and were decorated with ornate carvings. The king is going up the extra wide staircase on his horse, so that his feet don't touch the ground.

Aztecs

Like the Maya, the Aztecs built spectacular stone cities like Tenochtitlan with large pyramids dedicated to their gods. In the marketplace people would meet to trade goods and food. Feast days were very busy!

This mask is of the god Xipe Totec and is made from stone.

The Aztecs used stamps to print patterns on clothing or even their own bodies!

This turquoise double-headed serpent is made from mosaic.

This sculpture is of Mictlantecuhtli, the Aztec god of death.

Ancient Britain

Over 2,000 years ago, families in ancient Britain lived in roundhouses made from wood, with thatched straw roofs. These people were farmers, so they kept lots of animals like pigs, cows, sheep, goats and horses. They were good at making things like tools, jewellery and weapons. Even their shields were decorated!

This bronze fitting decorated a shield used to protect warriors in battle.

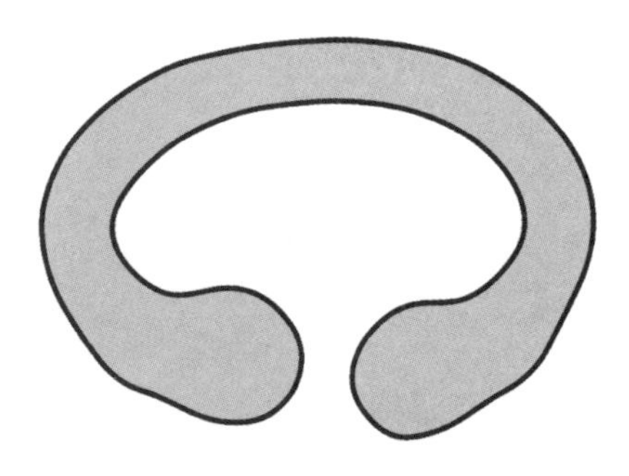

This neck-ring is made from gold and silver and weighs as much as a bag of rice.

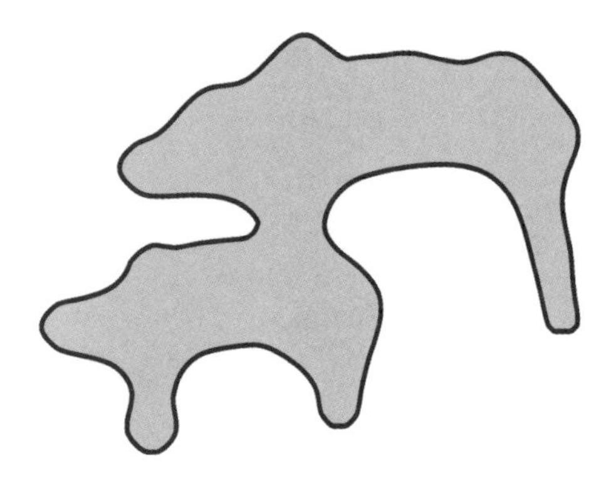

Look at these bronze boar models from the Iron Age.

Medieval Britain

In medieval Britain, wealthy people had grand banquets with many different kinds of food. They sometimes even ate exotic birds like swan and peacock! Each banquet had lots of courses and there would usually be music and entertainment between each one.

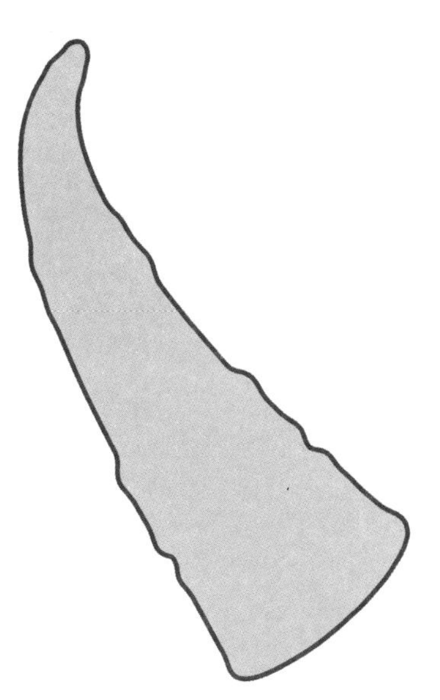

This hunting horn is made from elephant ivory.

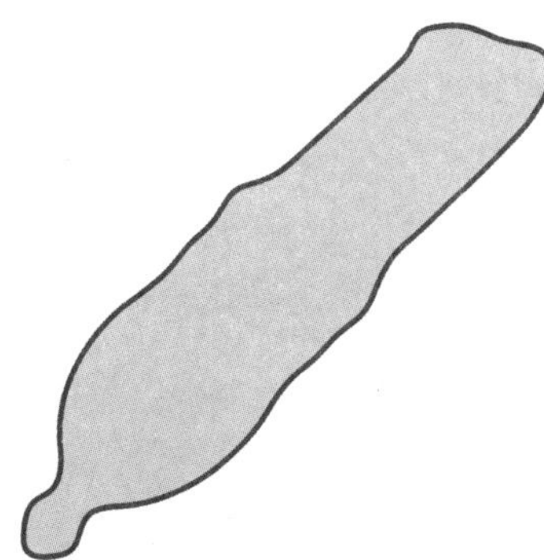

This musical instrument, called a *citole*, was a bit like a guitar, but was turned into a violin over 300 years later.

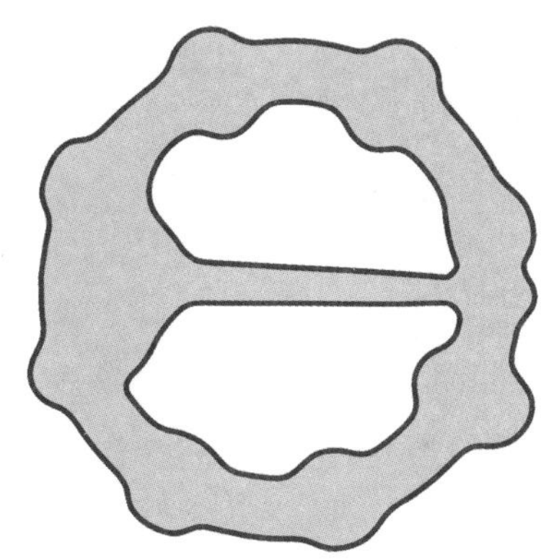

Here is a gold brooch with rubies and sapphires. It is engraved with the message: "I am here in the place of the friend I love."

India

In India, when rich people got married there were large wedding processions outside grand buildings. People even rode on elephants! Can you see the Taj Mahal in the distance? It is made of white marble and has a large dome that looks like an onion!

This necklace is made from cloth and gemstones.

This is a bronze sculpture of dancing Shiva, a Hindu god.

The Gazi Scroll is made up of 54 painted panels that tell a story full of amazing animals.

Solomon Islands

Solomon Islands is a country of many different islands and peoples in the southwest Pacific. People who live on the coasts use canoes for fishing and travelling. In the old days they made canoes of planks like the decorated canoe shown here, but nowadays they make dugout canoes or buy fibreglass ones.

Bowls like these are used to make vegetable puddings to eat with fish.

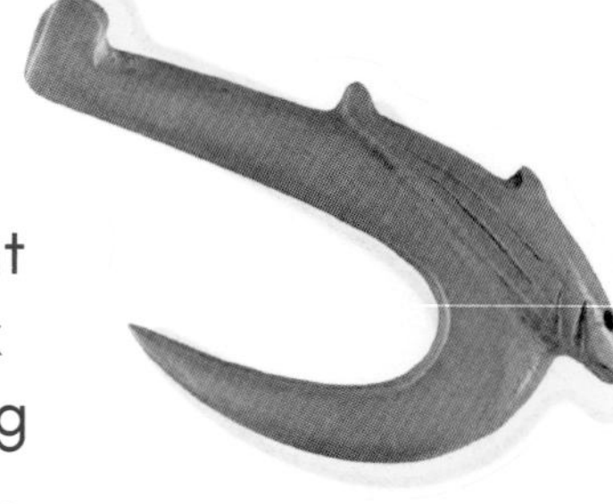

Fish are caught from the back of canoes using hooks and line.

Bonito (tuna fish) is an important food – this one is made from coconut shell.

Look at this wooden carving of a dangerous sea spirit!

Thailand

In many parts of South East Asia, people perform shadow puppet shows with brightly-coloured puppets made from animal skin. In Thailand, the shadow theatre is a way of telling moral stories with puppets, songs and chants.

Shadow puppets were made in the shape of all kinds of animals – this one is a tiger!

Here is a shadow puppet of Garuda – a mythical bird.

This horse shadow puppet is made from buffalo hide, bamboo and string.

Index

France p. 20-21

Casket
Limoges, France
About 1180

The Royal Gold Cup
France
1370-1380

Seal matrix and impression
France
1200-1400

Ivory mirror case
France
1300-1400

Ancient Greece p. 22-23

Horse sculpture from the Parthenon
Athens, Greece
438-432 BC

Silver coin
Macedonia, Greece
500-411 BC

Gold ear-rings
Athens, Greece
420-400 BC

Ancient Greece p. 24-25

Terracotta theatre mask
Melos, Greece
200-1 BC

Black-figured amphora
Attica, Greece
570-550 BC

The Siren Vase
Attica, Greece
480-470 BC

New Zealand p. 26-27

Greenstone hand club
New Zealand
Pre-1860

Carved wooden lintel
New Zealand
1830-1840

Maori cloak
New Zealand
1800-1900

Wooden Birdman kite
Bay of Plenty, New Zealand
1800-1850

Persia p. 28-29

Armlet from the Oxus Treasure
Tajikistan
500-300 BC

Wall tile
Iran
1800-1900

Gilt silver rhyton
Turkey
500-400 BC

Fragment of limestone relief
Persepolis, Iran
400-300 BC

Aztec p. 30-31

Stone mask
Mexico
1300-1521

Bird-shaped printing stamp
Mexico
1300-1521

Double-headed serpent mosaic
Mexico
1400-1521

Stone figure
Mexico
1325-1521

Ancient Britain p. 32-33

Bronze shield fitting
London, UK
350-150 BC

The Snettisham Great Torc
Norfolk, UK
150-50 BC

Bronze boars
London, UK
150-50 BC

Medieval Britain p. 34-35

Savernake Horn
Wiltshire, UK
1100-1350, with later additions

Citole
England, UK
1280-1330

Gold brooch
France
1200-1300

India p. 36-37

Necklace
India
About 1900

Dancing Shiva figure
Thanjavur, India
About 1100

The Gazi Scroll
India
About 1800

Solomon Islands p. 38-39

Wooden bowl
Solomon Islands
Pre-1870

Pearlshell fish-hook
Solomon Islands
Pre-1914

Fish figure made from coconut
Solomon Islands
Pre-1891

Wooden sea spirit figure
Solomon Islands
Pre-1893

Thailand p. 40-41

Tiger shadow puppet
Thailand
1965-1969

Garuda shadow puppet
Thailand
Mid-1970s

Horse shadow puppet
Thailand
Mid-1970s

Kenya
China
Ancient
Egypt
Ancient
Egypt
Maya

France
North America
Japan
Ancient Rome
Ancient Rome

Aztec
Persia
ew Zealand
Ancient
Greece
Ancient
Greece

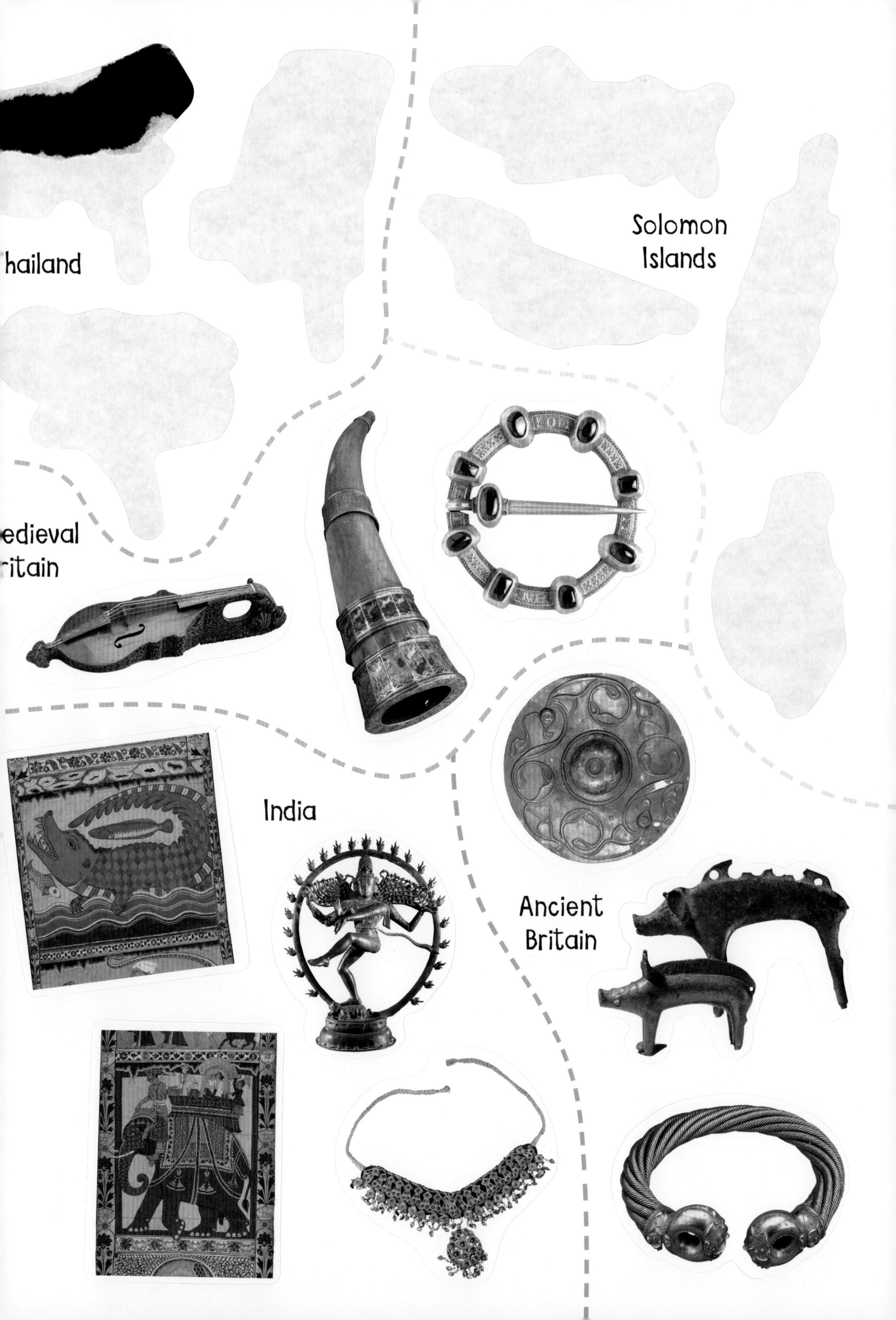

hailand
Solomon Islands
edieval ritain
India
Ancient Britain